THE
ISLAND HOPPERS

Douglas Arthur Brown

Boularderie
Island Press

Cover Layout by ON TIME Design harvegrant@gmail.com
Editor: Patricia O'Neil
Illustrations: Josh Kaiser

Library and Archives Canada Cataloguing in Publication

Brown, Douglas Arthur, author
    The island hoppers / Douglas Arthur Brown.

ISBN 978-1-926448-09-1 (paperback)
    I. Title.

PS8553.R684967I75 2016   jC813'.54   C2015-905624-1

www.douglasarthurbrown.com

A Boularderie Island Press Publication
www.boularderieislandpress.com

Printed in Canada

Table of Contents

Other titles by Douglas Arthur Brown

Juvenile

The Magic Compass
Archibald's Boo-boo

Adult

A Deadly Harvest
The Komodo Dragon and other stories
Quintet
Seeds

The lack of belief is a defect that ought to be concealed when it cannot be overcome.

Jonathan Swift

Introduction

Until the retreat of the last 'ice age' 11,000 to 10,000 years ago, many small islands existed in the vast waters of the North Atlantic Ocean. As the glaciers and ice sheets melted, ocean waters began to rise. Most of those small islands slipped into the sea, never to rise again.

Until now it was believed that those islands were never inhabited.

Enter the *Island Hoppers*.

What you are about to read in the pages of this book will enlighten you, no doubt delight you, and most certainly surprise you. By opening a window that has been closed for over 10,000 years, this astonishing narrative will debunk the long-held belief that those tiny North Atlantic islands were desolate and uninhabitable. You will see for yourself that, before the great glaciers began to melt and the Atlantic waters swelled, life did exist there.

On these islands lived several species of creatures called Entities, each with its own unique physical traits, personalities, and capabilities. Like Homo sapiens, the Entities were members of the Hominid family of mammals, but separate and distinct from humans. While there were certain similarities between the Entities and humans, the Entities possessed many extraordinary characteristics all their own.

Where the Entities originated from, and how they got to the islands in the North Atlantic, is not yet known, although research is ongoing. Our story begins on the islands at a time when great hardship was befalling the Entities. Realizing their island homes were sinking into the ocean, they set out in search of new frontiers. They trekked over ice bridges and paddled their handmade rafts for months, perhaps years, until finally they found their new home. It was a beautiful island, large enough for all of them, with vast resources to meet their needs. That island was what we now know as *Cape Breton*, lush with trees and meadows and surrounded by a sea brimming with fish.

How is it, then, that we are only now, 10,000 years later, coming to know of these creatures? Surely archaeologists and historians could not have overlooked such a significant chapter in our natural history.

The answer to this is simple, and lies in the fact that the Entities left behind very little by way of evidence to verify their existence. The few clues and remnants that did survive are so obscure, so well disguised by their striking similarity to human artifacts, scientists understandably mistook them as our own.

Had it not been for the discovery of the *Bren Parchments*, the Entities would have remained the world's best kept secret.

The *Brens* were one of the seven species of Entities, and arguably the most intelligent as they were the only Entity that kept records. They recorded not only their own activities, but also what they observed of the other Entities: the *Yrtles, Hhorts, Selch, Gnags, Tomboms* and *Velyns*.

Since they did not have a written language as such, the *Brens* recorded their history by etching symbols into strips of carefully preserved bark. In the fifteenth century these bark etchings were discovered and handed over to scholars who decoded and translated them into what became known as the *Bren Parchments*.

The journey of the *Bren Parchments* is long and mysterious, and the story of how they came into the author's possession is a tale for another time. What is clear is this: these parchments have given us a ten-thousand-year-old snapshot into the lives of these remarkable creatures, so unlike any beings seen before or since. The following narrative arose from those parchments, and is the very first published account — the debut so to speak — of the *Island Hoppers.*

Prepare yourself for the discovery of a lifetime!

Ice Ages

20,000 years ago, half of North America was covered in an ice sheet that was 1,000 feet thick in places. Ice ages are periods in Earth's history when glaciers and sea ice cover most of the planet's surface. The Earth has experienced five major ice ages since it formed several billion years ago. The term *ice age* is often used to describe a period when ice sheets cover parts of the northern and southern hemisphere, such as *Greenland* and *Antarctica*. By this definition we are currently living in an ice age! Within an ice age there are spans of time when temperatures are cooler (glacial periods) or warmer (interglacial periods). We are currently living in an interglacial period. From about 1300 – 1850 the northern hemisphere was much colder than today and was known as the *Little Ice Age*.

Entity Presence on Cape Breton Island

1. Baddeck / Uisge Ban Falls
2. Bay St. Lawrence
3. Bird Islands
4. Boularderie
5. Bras d'Or Lakes
6. Cheticamp
7. Fourchu
8. Framboise
9. Franey Mountain
10. Gull Cove
11. Kelly's Mountain
12. Margaree Valley
13. Point Michaud
14. The Pinnacle
15. White Hill
16. White Point

Note: Locations are approximate

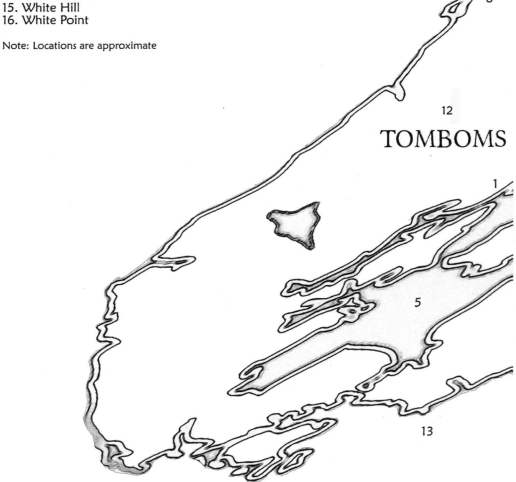

TOMBOMS

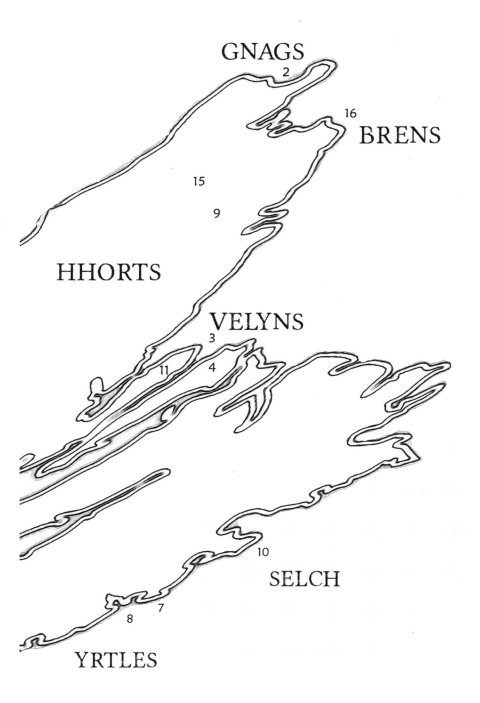

GNAGS

2

16

BRENS

15

9

HHORTS

VELYNS

3

11 4

10

SELCH

7

8

YRTLES

BRENS

brens/. Slept in fifteen-year cycles and could leap 27 feet.

Brens ranged in size from five-and-a-half to six feet tall. They were brown eyed and their body, including the face, was covered in fine hair, similar to the velvet on deer antlers. Females were a slightly darker colour than males. Lips were a deep purple, as were the eyelids, fingernails, and toenails.

Brens matured quickly, often within the first five years after birth. Young Brens learned by carefully observing and imitating the actions of older Brens.

Brens slept in fifteen-year cycles. Because of this there was little interaction between males and females as either all of the males or all of the females were asleep, except for a brief period between sleep cycles when both males and females were awake. Young Brens joined the long sleep cycles of the adults only when they reached physical maturity.

Brens possessed a unique joint beneath the balls of their feet that, when extended, filled with highly pressurized air. It provided extra spring action when the Brens leapt.

Brens had excellent hearing but did not like loud or sudden noises. They sought shelter during thunderstorms, stopping up their ears with dry eelgrass to avoid the painful rumble from thunderclaps. Nor did they like strong vibrations, as the tremors from earthquakes upset their balance, often resulting in a shattered eardrum, followed by death.

Brens were territorial, fiercely defending their villages against intruders, especially the *Hhorts*, ferocious creatures feared by all. Understandably, with half of their adult population asleep and defenceless most of the time, Brens had to be vigilant against attacks. However, the Brens did not initiate invasions or war.

During battle, Brens wore necklaces of dried bloodroot.

The Brens established trading relationships with most of the other Entities that made their homes on the island.

Brens settled in the area of *White Point* where there was an abundant supply of stone, which they used to construct vaults for the sleeping Brens. The vaults were located at the centre of their villages. Longhouses made of logs, where waking Brens lived, ringed the vaults.

Dry eelgrass was used as insulation around Bren longhouses during the winter to keep out icy winds and snow. As well, sleeping Brens were wrapped in

Limitations of migration

Young Brens quickly learned that if they spun their bodies in circles, they became nauseous. Brens were very sensitive to vibration and susceptible to vertigo. All known Bren settlements were located north of the equator where the Earth rotates at 1,000 mph. *Cape Breton Island's* rate of rotation (750 mph.) was very agreeable to the Brens.

Storytelling and language

Brens were storytellers. During their mate's fifteen-year hibernation cycles, Brens related stories to the sleeping Brens about the day-to-day events in the community. The stories wove themselves into their dreams, which were remembered upon waking.

14

Brens, like all Entities, did not have tails.

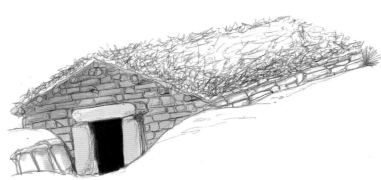

loose layers of fresh, moist eelgrass. As they slept, their wet breath prevented the seaweed from drying out. Toward the end of a sleep cycle, their breath became hot and dry and the eelgrass lost its moisture. The parched atmosphere within the vaults then triggered the awakening of the Brens.

Brens consumed great quantities of water. They particularly enjoyed icy water. They were experts at seeking out *cold spots* which appeared in deep crevices in rocks. Water seeped into the cracks, evaporated, and provided a constantly cool temperature. It was in these *cold spots* that the Brens kept their water chilled during the summer months.

Brens gathered ferns for nourishment, especially the cinnamon fern root with its white, crispy core and nutty flavour. Their diet also included mayflower and Labrador tea, butterwort, seaside plantain, and sea-lungwort.

They used fern fronds as well for cleaning the hard-packed floors of their longhouses and for dusting sleeping Brens.

As to clothing, the Brens wore little. The fine hair that covered their bodies provided adequate protection from the elements.

Sleeping Bren wrapped in eelgrass.

The Uisge Ban Falls Parliament

Uisge Ban is Gaelic for *white water*. The fifty-foot high *Uisge Ban Falls* is located at the end of a spectacular gorge fifteen kilometres north of the village of *Baddeck* in central *Cape Breton*. Before reaching the falls, hikers will pass through a widening of the valley that is scattered with dozens of large boulders.

It was here among these boulders that the *Brens* congregated for their parliament. The gathering took place once every fifteen years during the brief period when both females and males were awake.

To a hiker, these great boulders might appear randomly strewn throughout the valley bed. However, when viewed from above, it is evident that there is a distinct ring formation. It was here, thousands of years ago, that Bren elders sat on selected stones within this circular rock chain, and held their parliament. The Brens called this inner circle the *arena*. It was in this *arena* that the Brens aired their grievances and addressed the court elders on matters of communal interest. When everyone in the community had their say, the elders called for a recess and retired to the pools at the foot of the falls. For three sunrises they pondered what they had heard, and settled the disputes that arose during the parliament. In the elders' absence, the other Brens enjoyed a three-day festival during which pairings were arranged between younger Brens of mating age.

At the end of the festival, all of the Brens rejoined the elders at the falls to hear their decrees for the coming fifteen years. Those Brens who were about to enter the sleeping cycle then waded into the pools at the foot of the falls and submerged themselves in the water. When this ceremony was complete, all the Brens left the valley and returned on foot to their settlement at *White Point*, which was a considerable distance from *Uisge Ban Falls*. The fatigue from the long trek enabled the Brens who were about to enter the hibernation cycle to fall asleep immediately upon their return.

HHORTS

yourts /. Fiercest and most war-like of all the Entities.

Hhorts varied in size, from a relatively short stature of just under five feet to the more typical adult height of five-and-a-half feet. They were hairless with thick plum coloured leathery skin. The left and right side of the skull, collarbones, rib cages and femurs had a marked protrusion covered with thin, translucent skin. The chalky white bones were clearly visible through the hide.

Although scrawny in appearance, the Hhorts were strong and sinewy. They could bear heavy weights without apparent effort and uprooted stout tree trunks with their bare hands. In spite of their strength, they moved slowly and did not run. They had a lifespan of about forty years.

Hhorts moulted every five years. The leathery skin became jelly like, semi-transparent, and lost all pigment, revealing muscle and organs beneath the moulting skin. The *Brens* described it as, *"looking upon a creature that had been skinned alive, only this creature was walking and barring its teeth."* However, the painful transition was swift, the new epidermis replacing the old one within forty-eight hours.

Hhorts had a bowel movement only once every fourteen to sixteen weeks.

The muscle in the ears of a Hhort was well developed, allowing the ears to perk up like dogs' ears and listen for the footsteps of their enemies. Hhorts also possessed a long, hinged tongue containing fourteen bones. The powerful tongue pushed food quickly to the back of the throat.

Hhorts were pillagers, aggressive and prone to violent acts during their raids. Any creature that stood in their path was killed. Like an invasion of locusts, Hhorts' raids were relentless. The attacking Hhorts were unwavering in their assault, never veering from their chosen path as they advanced. The Hhorts' mission was to devour the food stores and crops of other Entities. A swift, violent death befell any victim who tried to protect its food. When all food in a settlement was gone, the ruthless Hhorts retreated.

Smell

A Hhort had no sense of smell because the lining of its nose was dry. Without mucous, the nose cannot detect smell.

Shedding

When Hhorts were shedding, they looked for talus deposits. Talus, or *scree*, is the weathered rock debris at the bottom of a steep mountain. Hhorts congregated in these areas, rubbing their skin with the talus to hasten moulting. (One popular talus location that still exists is in the *Cape Breton Highlands National Park*, just north of *Cheticamp* at the foot of *French Mountain*.)

To further ease the moulting process, Hhorts also covered their skin with crushed bayberry fruit, the waxy berries offering the new epidermis protection against infection.

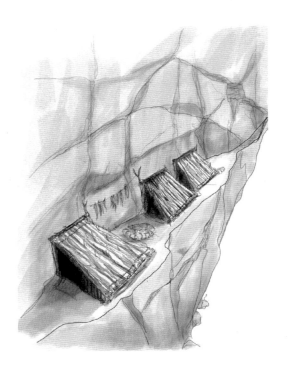

Hhorts were mountain-dwelling Entities, preferring hilltops. The *Brens* reported Hhort settlements in the mountains surrounding the *Cheticamp Flowage* in the *Cape Breton Highlands*, specifically *The Pinnacle*, *White Hill* and *Franey Mountain*.

Hhorts lived in lean-to huts, sharply pitched, attached to cliff sides. Hhort families were large, making it necessary for them to sleep tightly huddled in one hut. Younger Hhorts sometimes perished during the night, falling to their death if accidentally pushed out of the lean-to. The larger the family, the higher the status within the clan. The largest families were housed closest to mountaintops; smaller families settled along the hillsides below.

When a young Hhort reached maturity it left the settlement of its birth. It was called a *walker* because it wandered alone for many months before seeking a new home. If there were no other *walkers* present within its new settlement, it erected a lean-to at the bottom of the mountainside. It waited until it was joined by another *walker* and then mated. Once the pair established a family, they built higher on the mountain. Depending on the number of offspring, they rose within the hierarchy of their new community.

Roots were the mainstay of the Hhort diet. When the undergrowth in their hilltop forests became sparse, they pillaged the settlements of other Entities. Oddly, most of what they consumed during their raids was not root based, but palatable. Once they gorged on the provisions of other Entities, Hhorts returned to their mountain villages and the food they

When Hhorts were born they inherited the battle scars of their parents; the more scars a baby Hhort possessed, the greater the chance that it would grow up to be a mighty warrior.

had consumed sustained them for several seasons, allowing the root systems in their settlements to replenish. Hhorts also ate club moss, royal fern fiddleheads, yellow mountain saxifrage, dog lichens, and fire moss.

The preferred time for Hhorts to launch an attack was during overcast skies, as they could not tolerate stepping into the shadows cast by other living creatures. *Brens*, coming upon solitary *walkers*, used their shadows to block the lone Hhort from discovering their settlements. Eventually the *walker*, frightened by the shadows, retreated.

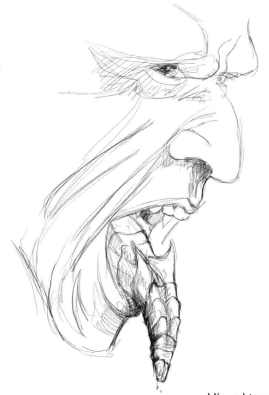

Hinged tongue

Legendary Islands

In the distant past, a series of islands were scattered throughout the North Atlantic Ocean. These islands were the ancestral homes of the Entities who travelled from island to island as circumstances warranted. As the *Glacial Period* retreated, some of the islands became uninhabitable or sank, and the Entities sought new homes, eventually settling on *Cape Breton Island*.

Through the ages, mariners have reported many mysterious islands in the waters of the North Atlantic. The most interesting was *Hy-Brasil*. Shrouded in fog, it only appeared for a short period once every seven years when the fogs evaporated. Based on the seafarers' tales, the probable location of *Hy-Brasil* was west of *Ireland*. Several shoals were located in this area of the Atlantic Ocean, perhaps remnants of sunken islands.

In medieval times there were many myths about *The Island of Seven Cities*. Seven Spanish bishops, fleeing the Moors from Northern Africa who had conquered Spain, discovered the island and built seven cities. Legends claim that sailors, landing on the beaches, used sand to scour their pots and discovered grains of gold flowing between their fingers.

The *Isle of Demons*, situated off the coast of what is now Newfoundland, was supposedly inhabited by "monsters." It first appeared on a map in 1507 and vanished again from sea charts by the middle of the 17th century. Today, geologists assume the *Isle of Demons* was actually a series of

stone outcrops, which were nesting grounds for migrating birds. Early sailors mistook the cries of these unknown birds for monsters. Their first encounters with walruses and polar bears produced the same mistaken conclusion. Some of the stories refer also to "melodic chants" emanating from the shores.

Sea Travel

According to the legend of St. Brendan (c. 484 - c. 577), the Irish monk sailed for seven years in a *curragh*, a wooden boat covered with ox hides. Some historians believe he reached the shores of Newfoundland, using the islands of the North Atlantic as stepping-stones. In the 1970s, the Irish adventurer Tim Severin built a replica of a *curragh*, called *The Brendan*, and sailed it to Newfoundland, proving that St. Brendan could indeed have made that treacherous Atlantic crossing fifteen hundred years ago.

It is possible that the industrious *Gnags* used their knowledge of raft building to travel and perhaps ferry other Entities from island to island thousands of years before the voyages of St. Brendan. Other Entities, such as the *Hhorts*, may have used ice floes to travel between the islands.

Hudson's Bay Company

In his search for a shortcut to China (the legendary *Northwest Passage*), Martin Frobisher was said to have discovered *Buss Island*. However, future expeditions failed to find the island again. *The Hudson's Bay Company* was granted ownership of *Buss Island* by King Charles II. It was not until 1934 that the Company declared the island they owned did not exist.

curragh

Phoenician voyages

The Phoenicians had the methods and skills for ocean sailing. Around 330 BC, the Greek geographer and mathematician Pytheas apparently sailed out into the Atlantic and reached a land called *Thule* beyond Britain. *Norway, Orkney* and *Shetland* are the most probable locations for *Thule*. Thor Heyerdahl sailed across the Atlantic in reed boats called the *Ra I* and *Ra II* in 1969 and 1970 in order to prove that the ancient Egyptians were capable of crossing the Atlantic.

GNAGS

ga-NAGS/. Fond of tattoos and lived on rafts.

Gnags were powerful swimmers due to their unusually large lungs. Strong arm and leg muscles, as well as a second eyelid further enhanced their exceptional swimming ability. This second eyelid was transparent and covered the eyeball upon contact with moisture, enabling the Gnags to clearly see images underwater.

Gnags, unlike any of the other Entities, were very fond of tattoos. Young adults were tattooed on both sides (but not the middle) of their high foreheads. These tattoos consisted of several wavy lines that sometimes intersected. The number of lines varied from Gne to Gne, but the minimum was three. When an adult Gne entered mid-life, a second tattoo was applied. Eyebrows were shaved and a tattoo consisting of a unique design etched in a pinpoint pattern replaced the brows. Then, when the Gne approached the age of 75, hair was shaved from the centre of its head and a third tattoo was applied to the middle of the forehead and continued upward along the top of the head ending at the back of the skull. This final tattoo comprised a series of symbols, representing the achievements of the individual Gne throughout its life. Symbols varied in meaning, usually representing a Gne's offspring, immediate ancestors, and life craft.

The venom in a yellow jacket wasp's stinger was fatal to Gnags.

monkfish

Gnags were more listeners than talkers. They were an even-tempered Entity and showed little emotion. They did not mourn their dead and exhibited no outward sign of distress when injured or in pain. The *Brens* recorded the following: "*A Gne fell upon a fishing spear, the tapered end piercing its stomach. The tip of the spear had two inverted hooks so if the Gne tried to pull it out, the hooks would shred the flesh. So the Gne pushed the spear through the stomach and out the other side. As yellow blood gushed from the wound, the Gne stood silently, carefully wiping the spear clean of blood before wandering away to tend its wound.*"

The mainstay of the Gnags' diet was fish and shellfish, supplemented by berries.

Their clothing was stitched from fish skin, usually from the hides of shark, cod, halibut and monkfish. Because the Gnags' diet was mainly fish, they were the only Entity that escaped marauding Hhorts. As Hhorts did not consume fish, they had no reason to attack the Gnag villages.

Gnags also ate shellfish such as Northern moon-shells, quahog, green sea urchins, Atlantic surf, rock and soft-shell clams, blue mussels, common rock barnacles and oysters.

Gnags lived in 'floating villages', building their dwellings on rafts. The raft communities were anchored in sheltered coves that allowed for easy access to the open sea but also provided cover from storms. Land-based activities were largely restricted to forays into forests to gather wood for the rafts, pigments for their tattoo dyes, and berries.

The raft communities were small, often made up of no more than three or four families, each living on its own raft. A larger raft or *stage* was at the centre of the moorings and used for communal activities.

Smaller rafts were launched from the floating villages for fishing expeditions.

The rafts were propelled by oars in deep waters and poles in shallow water. During the spring and summer, the floating settlements travelled from cove to cove. They overwintered in coves or bays not occupied by other floating settlements. Sometimes different villages gathered in the coves to participate in trade or to arrange pairings between young Gnags of mating age. Male Gnags always joined the families of their female mates.

Bay St. Lawrence was home to the only Gnag settlement that remained stationery. It was the largest raft village, almost filling the bay. All Gnags visited this settlement at least three times during their lives. The Gnags received their tattoos here, as it was where the master tattooists resided. This settlement was also home to the finest artisans who fashioned jewelry from shell and beach stone.

Tattoos

Gnag artists used a variety of colours in creating tattoos. Blue inks were made from blueberries and blackberries. Dandelions and goldenrod were used for yellow, and rich greens came from seaweed. Charcoal was used for black. Purple, one of their favourite colours, was made from the crushed shells of dog winkles and oyster drills, gathered at the seashore.

Curing

Gnags wore clothing made from the skins of fish. One technique for making this leather involved removing the flesh from the skins and soaking them in a mixture of stale urine and water. The ammonia in the urine drew the fat out of the skins. The skins (leather) were flattened on boards and dried, then kneaded to make them soft enough to sew.

The Bren Parchments

During the 1,000 years that they inhabited Cape Breton Island, the *Brens* recorded their history and that of the other Entities by etching symbols into strips of bark parchment. The parchments were sealed in clay cylinders and stored in a cave where they remained untouched for over 10,000 years.

Before John Cabot landed in *Cape Breton* in 1497, Portuguese navigators visited the shores to harvest the rich fish stocks. Improvements in shipbuilding and navigation allowed for longer voyages to explore lucrative trade routes. Knowledge of these voyages was kept secret to protect commercial interests.

It was on one of these voyages that Portuguese navigators discovered the cave where the *Bren Parchments* were hidden.

At this time, the port of *Bristol, England* was the busiest trade centre in Europe and it was here that the Portuguese navigator sold the *Bren Parchments* to a *Bristol* merchant. The *Bristol* merchant employed the services of several trusted scholars who deciphered the symbols on the *Bren Parchments*. They were intrigued by a passage in the parchments that referred to "yellow blood" that flowed in the veins of the *Gnags*. The merchant considered the possibility that the yellow blood was actually liquid gold. If one of these Entities were captured and taken to *Bristol*, perhaps it could be bled regularly with leeches. The gold blood would then be wrung from the leech and hardened to form nuggets to sell. The *Bristol* merchant and the scholars called themselves the *Custodians* of the *Bren Parchments* and swore not to share their knowledge of the *Bren Parchments* with outsiders.

The early *Custodians* set sail for the far shores of the North Atlantic in search of a mysterious island (*Cape Breton*) where the *Bren Parchments* claimed the Entities thrived. However, no living Entity was found on the island. By the time the *Custodians* arrived, the Entities had been absent from the island for thousands of years.

Bloodletting and barber poles

From antiquity to the late 19th century, the withdrawal of blood known as *bloodletting* was the most common medical procedure performed by healers and surgeons. It was based on a belief that blood and other fluids of the body called "humours" had to be kept in balance for good health.

During the Renaissance in Europe, bloodletting was often performed by barbers. The red and white striped barbershop pole originally represented blood-stained bandages wrapped around a pole.

Bloodletting reached its peak in the 19th century. France alone imported over 40 million leeches per year during the 1830's.

Today leeches are used to assist in the healing of skin grafts and even in reattaching severed fingers and toes. As the leech feeds on blood through its suckers, it releases a blood thinner that prevents blood from clotting under the skin grafts and increases blood circulation to the veins in the fingers and toes.

The *Rosetta Stone* was carved in 196 BC using the three scripts of the time. Hieroglyphic, which was the script used for important or religious documents; Demotic, which was the common script of *Egypt*; and Greek, the language of the rulers of *Egypt* at that time.

The stone was found by Napoleon's soldiers in a town called *Rosetta* (*Rashid*) in the *Nile delta*. Jean-François Champollion finally deciphered the hieroglyphs in 1822. Because the *Rosetta Stone* was written in three scripts all bearing the same message, scholars were able to decipher the hieroglyphic text by comparing it to the other scripts. Without the *Rosetta Stone* it is possible that the ancient Egyptian hieroglyphics would never have been deciphered.

Two other famous scripts remain a mystery to this day. The Indus script refers to short strings of symbols associated with the *Indus Valley Civilization* (modern day *Pakistan* and northwest *India*) in use between the 26th and 20th centuries BC. Rongorongo is a system of glyphs discovered in the 19th century on *Easter Island*. It cannot be read despite numerous attempts at decipherment.

VELYNS

vel-OONS/. Communicated through musical chants, not words.

Male Velyns had a lifespan of about 60 years, but females generally lived up to 80 years. Females were slightly taller and heavier than males and both had long torsos. All Velyns had considerable upper body strength, particularly the arms, which were muscular.

Velyns had an appendage called a *pitch* at their throat. It was a lobe of flesh like that found on wattle birds. Normally it was smooth and flat, but Velyns could inflate it with air from their lungs to produce melodic sounds.

The Velyns were the only Entity that purposely created a punishment meant to "mark" a law-breaker: pinching the *pitch*. This produced a deep blue bruise, which was very visible and resulted in public humiliation. The offender was shunned until all traces of bruising disappeared. Once the *pitch* healed and returned to normal, so too did the Velyn's status within the clan. Velyns were always in the company of each other. Therefore, the threat of being shunned was a powerful deterrent to disharmony in their society.

Unity was important among Velyns and nowhere was this more evident than in their celebration of vocal harmony, as they were a musical Entity.

Music, expressed through chanting and elaborate airs, was a crucial factor in determining where Velyns settled. Small Velynian villages dotted both sides of the shores of the *Great Bras d'Or channel*, stretching from *Kempt Head* to *New Campbellton*. *Kelly's Mountain*, and to a lesser extent, the hills of *Boularderie East*, acted as a natural amplifier, bouncing the melodic Velynian voices along the channel from settlement to settlement. All music was sung *a Capella*, as Velyns did not make musical instruments. Velyns used the *pitch* at their throat to modulate their voices. Some songs and chants were barely audible, while others, especially symphonic-like compositions sung by many voices, carried for miles in all directions. Hearing a village of Velyns raise their voices in song mesmerized the listener. *Gnags* were so taken with the music they often altered their navigation, as if drawn to the *Great Bras d'Or channel* by the music, anchoring their floating settlements nearby. It was only when the Velyns quieted their voices that the *Gnags* left the channel to continue their voyages.

Velyns were superior climbers. They could scale cliffs, hillsides, and trees with ease. Since the Velynian diet consisted largely of bird eggs, their scaling skills enabled them to reach high nests.

Sheep Laurel

This plant is toxic, and if ingested can cause nausea, vomiting, sweating, abdominal pain, headache, convulsions, and paralysis. However, Velyns experienced only one effect from the plant: watering of the eyes and nose. This actually proved beneficial to the Velyns since the secretion of water cleared their nasal passages, throat, and *pitch*, which produced richer chants.

Puffin

Velyns did not eat eggs from the nests of birds with hooked beaks (flesh-eaters, such as eagles or hawks).

Their diet also included turtle eggs, blueberries, broad-leaf cattail, sweet gale, one-flowered shinleaf, and cranberries.

Velyns built their dwellings partially underground. A hole was dug four to six feet into the earth. The walls of this rectangular pit were insulated with leaves and feathers. Bricks, used to create walls, were made from bundles of dry, tightly compacted leaves, and stacked above the foundation. Ropes made from the fibres of dead plants such as dogbane and milkweed were tightly twisted to create a roof across the top of the walls.

Velyns traded mostly with *Gnags*. The *Gnags* supplied rafts in exchange for the strong ropes Velyns created for scaling cliffs and trees. *Gnags* used the ropes to bind their floating villages; Velyns used the rafts for a single purpose — to reach the *Bird Islands* off *Cape Dauphin*.

The *Bird Islands* were an important nesting ground for several species of birds, among them the *puffin*. Velyns scaled the steep cliffs to access a plentiful supply of eggs from nesting birds.

Once each Autumn, during a full moon, young Velyns readying to leave the homes of their parents to start their own families, climbed to the top of the *Bird Islands* to stand and gaze upon the moon until dawn.

Sand

Adult Velyns often fed grains of sand to their offspring. The grit was beneficial to the development of a young Velyn's *pitch*.

Catching Insects

In addition to their fondness for eggs and berries, Velyns had an appetite for insects. By observing the shape of a bird's beak, Velyns could determine where the insects were in abundance. For instance, they sought out the nesting grounds of birds with thin, pointy beaks characteristic of insect-eaters such as warblers. They also followed birds with short, wide beaks, such as swallows, which fed in flight. When the swallows swooped low, especially when flying ants were abundant, Velyns ran beneath them, and scooped the insects from the air with long poles topped with fronds soaked in honey.

TOMBOMS

TOM-boms/. Only Entity that domesticated animals and farmed.

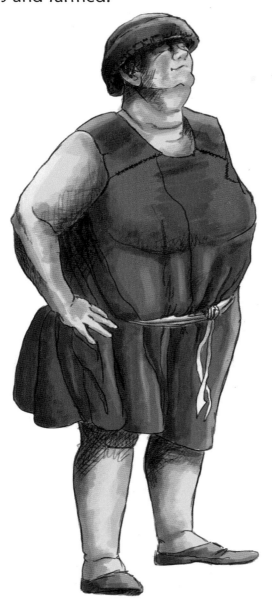

Tomboms were stocky with thick arms, legs, and necks. They had fat cheeks and fleshy eyelids. They were industrious and creative artisans, as well as skillful traders.

To visiting *Brens* and *Gnags*, Tomboms often appeared confused and disorganized. It was common to witness a family of Tomboms commence an activity, abandon it, try something different, and then return to the original task. *Brens*, on a trade mission, made the following observation: *"Five Tomboms were clearly headed in the direction of the river. After only walking three or four hundred feet, the party abruptly stopped and returned to their original starting position. After a few moments of confusion, they set off once again for the river, but only covered half the distance when one of their members veered off to the right. The remaining Tomboms quickly fell in behind the young male who seemed to lead them in circles several times."*

The observation of the *Brens*, noted above, was in fact a carefully structured problem-solving scenario where the Tombom youth tested all the options available as he chose a proper path to the river. Regardless of how confusing it appeared to the observing *Bren*, it was a classic exercise in trial and error.

Tomboms rarely disciplined their children and the eldest child was always consulted before any decisions affecting the household were made. The eldest child's authority was limited to family matters. Issues involving the well-being of the entire village were adult matters. Because Tombom society was a culture of skilled negotiators, children were trained in decision making from an early age.

Tomboms settled in the *Margaree Valley*. Their most frequent trading partners were the *Brens*, and to a lesser extent, the *Gnags*, who acted as trading emissaries on behalf of the *Velyns*. Tomboms were skilled toolmakers, potters, and weavers. They supplied *Brens*, *Gnags* and *Velyns* with knives, axes, awls, eyed needles, scrapers, pots, and baskets. Pottery, like the baskets, was coiled. Tomboms were also blacksmiths, forging ore in furnaces made from clay and fed with charcoal. The slag was removed from the iron by either chipping it away or brushing it off with a porous stone. It was then pounded into shape.

Skilled tailors, Tomboms produced bolts of felt made from hair and wool. The raw materials were combed out in layers on a dampened mat, rolled up and left for days, matting the fibres into a durable fabric for their clothing.

Morning dew

In Spring, Tombom children were observed gathering morning dew on a twig, swirled like cotton candy, and eagerly eaten.

The nasal index

There was an interesting relationship between the Entity nasal index and climate. Most of the Entities had relatively narrow and long noses, which were more efficient in warming the air before it reached the lungs; therefore, they were better suited to colder climates.

Tomboms engaged in limited farming, specifically the cultivation of herbs. These herbs were used for poultices to soothe tooth-and earaches; to relieve inflammation from burns and other skin irritations; for relief from the bites of animals, insects and body lice; and to draw out poison from infected cuts and scrapes.

They enjoyed teas. Older Tomboms boiled dandelion roots for several hours, producing a strong concoction that was drunk before sunrise. Younger Tomboms drank a tea made from mayflower leaves.

Another of the Tomboms favourite foods was the round bulb-like root of dwarf ginseng, which they boiled in salted water and ate cold like peanuts. Tomboms were the only Entity that ate meat, primarily bear and caribou. The animals were hunted with spears.

Tomboms infused non-aromatic flowers with their favourite scents by soaking the seeds in rose water. As the flowers grew, they emitted the scent of the rose water. Poultice bags were also infused with rose water scent.

Tomboms were also the only Entity that domesticated animals, for example geese, which were raised as companion animals. Young Tomboms were herded by snapping geese to prevent wandering while unattended. A gaggle of geese often followed adult Tomboms. Wantonly injuring a goose was an insult to the Tomboms. Visiting *Brens* and *Gnags* kept a watchful eye lest they agitate or hurt a goose. Even if the injury were accidental, the Tombom ceased all trading with the offending visitor.

Tomboms also raised small herds of Mastodons.

Yurt

On Mastodons

Mastodons travelled in herds and had a thick coat like musk oxen. Their diet consisted of a variety of vegetation, similar to what moose eat today. They had two sets of tusks, the upper tusks often six feet in length.

Adults were between 2.5 and 3 meters tall and weighed between 3500 and 5400 kilograms.

Mastodons roamed North America from 3.75 million to 11,000 years ago. They became extinct 11,000 to 10,000 years ago.

There are several theories as to why the mastodons became extinct. These theories include over-hunting by humans new to North America, or the diseases they brought with them. Climate change is another probability, which may have subjected mastodons to conditions adverse to their survival, and possibly eliminating food sources due to the warmer temperatures.

The first two mastodon fossils in *Nova Scotia* were uncovered in *Cape Breton*. A femur bone was discovered in *Lower Middle River*, *Victoria County*, circa 1833. The second was a molar tooth, found in 1895 at *Baddeck*.

The Evolution of the Island Hoppers

Like humans, the Entities belonged to the Hominid family of mammals, which also includes apes. The first common ancestor of the Entities and humans was the *Dryopithecus Ape*, which existed between 26–3 million years ago.

The Entities shared many common physical characteristics with humans. Their brains were highly developed. They walked upright and their legs were longer than their arms. The backbone was "S" shaped rather than bow shaped or straight. Hands were distinctive and used for manipulation rather than to assist in walking, and chins were distinct. As well, they possessed tools, often clothed themselves, and built complex structures to protect themselves from the elements.

However, there are marked differences. Humans do not have the bellowed pivot of a *Bren* foot, the hinged Hhort tongue, the cartilage of a *Yrtle* earlobe, the second eyelid of a *Gnag*, or a *Velynian pitch* in the neck. Some Entities matured at a faster rate than humans and some enjoyed a longer life span.

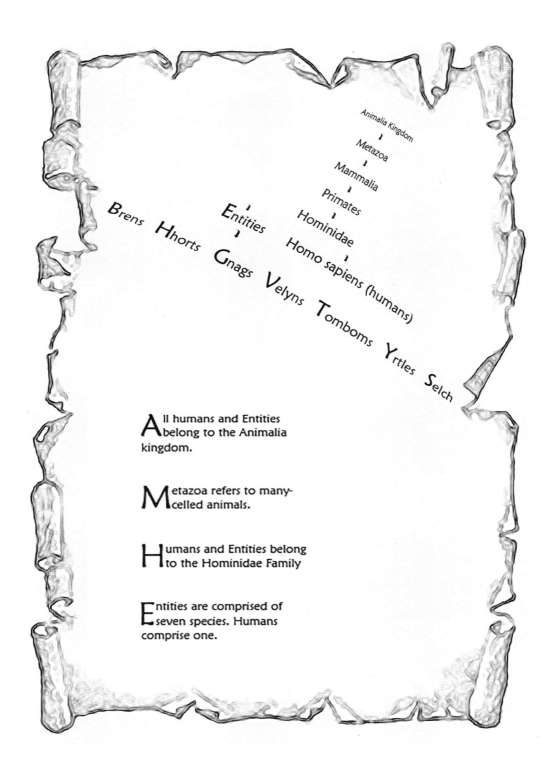

Animalia Kingdom

Metazoa

Mammalia

Primates

Hominidae

Entities   Homo sapiens (humans)

Brens Hhorts Gnags Velyns Tomboms Yrtles Selch

A ll humans and Entities belong to the Animalia kingdom.

M etazoa refers to many-celled animals.

H umans and Entities belong to the Hominidae Family

E ntities are comprised of seven species. Humans comprise one.

YRTLES

UR-dels/. Left hand was one-third larger than right hand.

Yrtles were the tallest of all the Entities. At maturity they reached a uniform height of six feet and an exact weight of 150 pounds. They had a greenish complexion and yellow eyes. They were born with a mane of hair that remained unchanged throughout their lives.

Most Yrtles matured in their third decade. However, some did not reach adulthood until the fourth or fifth decade of their 80-year lifespan.

A Yrtle's left hand was one-third larger than its right hand. Yrtles had no fingernails or toenails. From a distance, Yrtles looked as if they wore large oval-shaped studs in their earlobes. The studs were actually shiny cartilage, called *domes*, which covered the centre of the earlobe. The *domes* were sensitive to mood changes. Normally the *domes* were milky coloured, but Yrtles were rather skittish and prone to both agitation and excitement. Their moodiness caused the *domes* to change colour, ranging from the palest milky hues to brilliant emerald, turquoise, and amber.

Yrtles did not travel far from their villages at night if they were agitated or excited. The luminescence of the *domes* acted like beacons, making them easy prey for predators.

Although most of the other Entities attempted to engage Yrtles in trade, they ignored almost all outside contact, preferring to keep to themselves. They tolerated the occasional trade visit from *Brens* or *Gnags*, but they never visited the settlements of other Entities.

Yrtles spent their lives in non-verbal communication, preferring to use expressive gestures and body language. They exhibited a wide array of facial expressions, hand and arm gesticulations, and exaggerated body posturing when interacting.

Physical contact was also part of their communication ritual, especially during an intense discussion. To other Entities, this could be mistaken for a wrestling match as it involved much pummeling on the upper chest and shoulders. These actions appeared aggressive, even violent, but the Yrtles displayed no signs of distress or pain. When the exchange was finished, one of the Yrtles passed the fingers of its enlarged left hand against the open palm of its companion's left hand before walking away.

Yrtles were gifted mimics and able to imitate the sounds of animals and birds; for example, the snort of a rutting caribou or the cry of a startled loon.

Birth marks

Each time a female Yrtle gave birth, a mole appeared on the mother's upper arm. The number of moles corresponded to the number of her children. Black moles denoted male offspring and red moles signified females.

Swimming

Like *Gnags*, Yrtles were capable swimmers. They dove for dulse, their favourite food, often found attached to underwater rocks, ledges and other marine plants. In winter, Yrtles cut a hole in the ice to dive for the dulse. They could remain submerged for several minutes without suffering from hypothermia.

Yrtle settlements were located near the ocean, where fog and sea breezes were prevalent. They built villages along the shores of *Fourchu, Framboise* and *Point Michaud.* Their huts were low and used mostly for sleeping or waiting out a storm.

Yrtles always kept fires burning in front of their huts, even during the heat of summer. They liked to roll in the ash left behind from fires, rubbing the charcoal vigorously against exposed skin. Charcoal was also collected and applied to the interior walls of their huts. Yrtles were prone to infection from the bites of gnats and black flies, and the ash acted as a repellent.

Their diet consisted mainly of dulse, but in the summer they also collected beach peas and boiled them in salt water. Like most of the Entities, they collected berries and dried them to eat in winter or to season the dulse.

Oval cartilage in earlobe

Cocoons

Yrtles spent the first nine months of their life cocooned within their mane of hair. When the muscles in their hands became strong, they used their fingers to part their hair, allowing them to sit up.

Reflections

Yrtles did not have the ability to recognize reflections. *Brens*, on the other hand, would sit and ponder clouds and trees mirrored in a pond. Among the *Tomboms*, reflections bore an element of superstition. Tombom children were taught never to walk through a still pond. Instead, they walked around the water lest they disturb the image and bring bad luck upon themselves. In contrast, *Velynian* children cast stones into the water to watch happily as the picture "shattered".

SELCH

zelch/. Lived within stone fortification and had no contact with the other Entities.

The Selch were the most mysterious Entity on the island. A village of *Gnags*, rafting the waters off *Gull Cove*, *Gabarus* for the first time, spotted several dozen Selch walking the shoreline at dusk, each bearing a lit torch. They wore hoods that covered their faces and long cloaks that fell to their feet. When the Selch noticed the *Gnags* offshore, they immediately extinguished their torches and disappeared into the falling darkness.

The following year, as the *Gnags* sailed past *Gull Cove* in daylight, they saw an imposing fortification atop a grassy hill overlooking the cove. But there was no sign of the Selch, nor was there any sign of them for the next several years. They had left *Gull Cove*. Eventually, a party of *Gnags* took to the shore one Spring to explore the

abandoned fortification on the hill.

The fortification faced the sea. Within there was a stone building, one level and rectangular in shape. It measured 130 feet long by 60 feet deep, with a height of only twelve feet from floor to ceiling.

The stone building was surrounded by a wall constructed of timber. Between the wall and the front of the building was a courtyard, the ground covered with a layer of crushed seashells. Two tall stone monuments occupied the centre of the courtyard. The monuments were chiseled flat and smooth, and the moon in one of its four phases (first quarter, full, last quarter and new) was carved on each side of the monuments. Two gates constructed of massive logs were centred in the front outer wall. This was the only entrance to the fort. The gates opened inward and could be barred from either inside or outside. A gate barred from the inside would keep intruders out. A gate barred from the outside would prevent a prisoner, for example, from getting out.

The inside of the stone building had a hard-packed floor and no internal rooms or divisions. It was empty. The *Gnags* did not discover any signs of habitation such as beds, food stores or cooking utensils.

The *Gnags* never returned to this abandoned Selch fortification after this one and only visit.

The moon, like the sun, rises in the east and sets in the west. In the northern hemisphere, the sunlit side of the moon moves from right to left and in the southern hemisphere from left to right. The moon always keeps the same side facing the Earth, never allowing us to see the other side from Earth. In the first days after a new moon (a slim crescent) light reflected off the Earth by the sun onto the moon is called earthshine.

Gull Cove

In the 18th century, a fishing village was built on the site of the long-gone Selch fortification at *Gull Cove*. Stones used in building the foundations of the fishing huts can still be found here. Is it possible that some of the stones may have been left over from the rubble of the Selch fortification? A hiking trail, which begins just past the graveyard in *Gabarus*, leads to this site.

The Battle of White Point

White Point is located in northern *Cape Breton* at the eastern tip of *Aspy Bay*. According to the *Bren Parchments*, *White Point* was the site of the fiercest confrontation ever recorded between the *Hhorts* and another Entity—the *Brens*.

One spring, when a Bren scouting party failed to return to White Point after a month-long absence, the other Brens became concerned. Trackers were then sent out from White Point to investigate. The winter had been particularly harsh and it was feared the scouts had perished in an avalanche. However, the trackers, like the scouts, did not return.

The Brens at White Point feared the worst: an impending assault on their settlement by marauding Hhorts.

The Hhorts were mountain dwellers, and their villages dotted the peaks of *The Pinnacle*, *White Hill* and *Franey Mountain*, all to the south of White Point. The Brens assumed, and rightly so, that the Hhorts had marched through the highlands and were now following the shoreline north toward White Point.

The Hhorts ambushed the Bren scouts and trackers on their northward march. The scouts encountered them at *Ingonish* and the trackers somewhere north of there.

If the Hhorts arrived at the edge of the White Point settlement, the Brens could be trapped. One possibility of escape would be to plunge into the sea and tread water until the enemy retreated. Brens were strong swimmers and able to survive frigid waters for long periods of time.

71

But this was not feasible since Brens hibernated in fifteen-year cycles and could not be awoken prematurely from their slumber. Half the village, either all the males or all the females, was almost always in hibernation.

Abandoning the village in advance of the Hhorts' attack was another possibility. However, that too was not practical due to the sleep cycles. Each waking Bren would have to carry a sleeping Bren on its back, moving as carefully as possible so as not to rouse the sleeping Brens.

Although slow footed, Hhorts did not stop to rest until they reached the target of their attack. Unless they were well ahead of their enemy, the Brens, moving slowly and fatigued from the weight they carried, would certainly be overcome by advancing Hhorts.

Faced with these challenges, the Brens sent forth another party of trackers, this time prepared to find out how far the approaching Hhorts were from White Point. If they were still at a considerable distance from the village, the sleeping Brens could be evacuated to the safety of the *Gnag* settlement at *Bay St. Lawrence*. But the scouts returned before nightfall the same day they set out.

The Hhorts were close, no more than a day's walk from White Point, and there were many of them.

If the estimates of the trackers were correct, it would be the largest group of Hhorts ever to have marched on another Entity. Some travelled east from *The Pinnacle*, then were joined by others at *White Hill*, and more at *Franey Mountain*.

The severe winter had driven the Hhorts to the brink of starvation.

With less than a day to prepare for the siege, the Brens readied themselves as best they could. First, the females whispered into the ears of the sleeping males, who were in the hibernation cycle. This was to ensure that those who

survived the battle and awoke from their slumber would know of the disaster that had befallen their settlement, remembering the words that had been spoken to them while they slept.

Young Brens were sent north to safety and to warn the *Gnags* at *Bay St. Lawrence*, in case the Hhorts continued their march after pillaging White Point.

If the Hhorts had attacked any of the other Entities, they would have stepped aside and allowed the Hhorts to raid their storehouses. Hhorts only killed if there was resistance. It would cause hardship for a village if a season's provisions were stolen and devoured by the Hhorts, but their lives would at least be spared. However, the Brens had more to protect than food. Sleeping Brens were wrapped in eelgrass and Hhorts had been known to eat eelgrass. If the eelgrass cocoons were removed from sleeping Brens, it would upset the hibernation cycle and the Brens could die.

The Morning of the Battle

The Brens awoke to a heavy blanket of cloud, perfect weather for their enemies. Hhorts avoided shadows and did not launch an attack under a cloudless sky. They also became disoriented if clouds passed in front of the sun and cast fast-moving shadows across the battlefield. Unfortunately for the already terrified Brens, this dark, gray morning did not bode well.

The Hhorts were only hours away.

The Heralds Fall

The Heralds were the first on the battlefield and the first ones to fall. Bearing long poles with sails of black cloth, the Heralds bravely entered the battlefield in advance of the Bren warriors. This was a diversion, meant to confuse the front wave of Hhorts, who advanced shoulder to shoulder to prevent any of their victims from slipping past. The Hhorts, with their poor eyesight, mistook the billowing black cloths for shadows. The Hhorts scattered, thinning their ranks. It was a tactic taught to the *Gnags* by the *Velyns* and passed on to the Brens.

The Heralds broke through the front wave of Hhorts and continued toward the second wave, leaving openings in their wake that would allow the Bren warriors to get a foothold on the battlefield. By the time the Heralds reached the third of the four waves of advancing Hhorts, their proud banners began to fall. The Hhorts in the third wave fell upon their prey, viciously snapping the Heralds' necks between their fingers.

A Deadly Aim

The first line of Bren warriors, armed with short spears and a deadly aim, took up position in the wake of the Heralds' charge. The Hhorts in the first and second waves began to fall, their throats pierced before they could scream in anguish. The remaining Hhorts moved inward, in a vain attempt to fill in the gaps created by the Bren Heralds. They tried to corral the Brens who had broken their ranks, and strangle them before other Brens arrived. But the Brens lay down their spears as the slow-moving Hhorts approached

from left and right. They crouched on their haunches, and faced the third wave of Hhorts advancing onto the battlefield.

The Hhorts, thinking the Bren warriors had kneeled in defeat, bellowed in victory. There were other Bren warriors approaching from the settlement, but they were still far away. The Hhorts would have time to slay the cowardly Brens squatting in their midst before the others arrived.

The Long Spears

As the Hhorts moved closer to the crouching Brens, a second arsenal of spears was unleashed upon them. These were long spears, hurled by the Bren warriors approaching from the settlement. Like the weapons of those warriors who knelt silently on the battlefield, the long spears were quick to find their mark. Within minutes, the remaining Hhorts of the first and second waves were dead.

It was unfortunate for the Hhorts that they chose the Brens as their first victims in a hundred years. Next to the Hhorts, the Brens were the most powerfully built Entity on the island, able to throw a spear with a force and distance that surpassed any other weapon known. The Hhorts knew the Brens were formidable foes in hand-to-hand combat, but Hhorts had always had the advantage of stamina, defeating any enemy on the field through sheer persistence, fuelled by their battle rage and hunger. Now, those in the third and fourth waves watched in amazement, as a quarter of their army fell to the enemy.

However, the distance between the advancing Hhorts and the spear-throwing Brens was diminishing, and without that distance the impact of the deadly long spears was weakened. They could still wound the leathery skin of the Hhorts but not pierce the heart or throat. For this they needed distance and ceased hurling their spears.

Spring to Action

The Brens, who had remained crouching among the fallen Hhorts of the first and second wave, quietly raised their faces to the approaching enemy. In each hand, they clutched a dagger that they had carefully concealed. Slowly, they shifted their weight, flexing the powerful pivot joint in their feet. They sprang, leaping toward their enemy with such force that the Hhorts of the third wave were thrown on their backs. Before the Hhorts could recover from the fall, two daggers silenced them. In an instant the Brens pounced again, striking the Hhorts in the fourth wave. But because the Brens were now weakened by the exertion of their two leaps, they fell short of their targets and many were quickly trampled underfoot. Others barely had the strength to raise their daggers before their necks were snapped.

Final Assault

However, these brave warriors did not die in vain. Their actions allowed the rear lines of the spear-wielding Brens to gain the necessary distance between themselves and the Hhorts once again. The whistling spears struck down Hhorts in the final wave of their ranks.

The weak among the Brens had been instructed by the elders that should their warriors' final assault fail, they were to throw open the storehouse doors in hopes that the remaining Hhorts would fill their stomachs and go home without violating the vaults of the sleeping Brens. However, this proved not to be necessary. As the Bren warriors stood their ground, the sun emerged from behind the clouds. Gathering up the Heralds' fallen banners scattered at their feet, the warriors waved them in the air, casting shadows over the bloodied battlefield. The Hhorts retreated.

Tales Are Told

After the battle, the Brens attended to the dead, lighting pyres to honour the warriors who had fallen, and, less ceremoniously, to burn the bodies of their dead and dying enemies.

As the spring unfolded, and the ice in the bay melted, a flotilla of *Gnag* rafts arrived from *Bay St. Lawrence*, returning the young Brens who had been sent away for their protection. The *Gnags* were told the story of how the brave Brens defeated the fierce Hhorts at the Battle of White Point, all of which was recorded in the *Bren Parchments*. As to what happened to the retreating Hhorts, half-starved and weary with defeat, the story does not tell.

RUCE

The Ruce were not an Entity, but mythical creatures, lending themselves to many wild imaginings by the Entities. They appeared in the tales told by *Brens, Gnags, Tomboms, Yrtles* and *Velyns*. Each had its own vision of what these elusive creatures looked like and how they acted.

Brens held that the Ruce were the size of dragonflies. They had a fondness for hares and protected them, running behind the hare, cloaked within its shadow. If a *Bren* child tried to catch a hare, the Ruce pulled on the animal's tail, signaling it to turn left or right, leaving the child to tumble to the grass with empty arms.

Gnags only reported sightings of the Ruce in winter. The Ruce built flying boats with oars that looked like the wings of birds. They took to the sky when sea smoke rose over open waters on frigid winter days. Hidden within a flock of birds, the Ruce piloted their flying boats, riding the sea smoke like waves.

To the *Tomboms*, the Ruce were creatures of the night. In late spring and early summer

Tomboms listened for the sound of peepers, a small brownish tree frog that makes a shrill peeping call early in the evening. The Ruce called to each other, their voices disguised as frogs. They gathered in large numbers on these evenings to dance the night away. However, if a *Tombom* approached the celebration, the peeping stopped and the Ruce vanished. If a storm approached, the Ruce sought shelter by wrapping themselves in the leaves of poplar trees. When *Tomboms* passed these poplars with their leaves turned inside out, they knew bad weather was on its way but never dared disturb the Ruce for fear that lightning would strike.

On days when the air was rich with early moisture, *Yrtle* children eagerly searched for dew-laden spider webs, which were the birthing cradles of the newborn Ruce. The dew-cradles were signs of good weather, signifying that the rest of the day would be dry. If a *Yrtle* felt a sudden breeze on a still day, it was because a Ruce had run through it. If the breeze only hit the *Yrtle's* knees, it was a young Ruce, but if the breeze hit it full in the face, it was an adult Ruce.

Velyns knew when a Ruce had escaped the snapping pincers of sand crabs. Its tail hung to the ground, leaving furrows in the dunes of sandy beaches. The single grains of sand that rolled down the dunes encased the beads of perspiration that fell from the fear-stricken Ruce.

Acknowledgments

For Peter Thuesen — who shares my passion for the anthropology of gnomes, elves, and nisser.

Thank you to the early readers of this manuscript: Donna Troicuk, Bruce Brown, and Lars Willum.

And to Pat O'Neil who returns to edit her fourth of my seven books. My favourite quote from Pat after the first edit on *The Island Hoppers* is *"great material — wrong book."* Truer words were never spoken!